Bb Clarinet

A BEST IN CLASS CHRISTMAS

by Bruce Pearson and Chuck Elledge

Dear Student,

Welcome to **A BEST IN CLASS CHRISTMAS**! These festive yuletide selections have been especially written to provide you with years of enjoyment. Fill your holiday season with imaginative musical activities using the features of **A BEST IN CLASS CHRISTMAS**:

EVERY player has the Melody with WORDS.

Sing while others accompany your section during rehearsals and concerts.
Use the Piano/Vocal/Guitar book and sing with friends and family.

EVERY player has an A part which works as a solo with piano accompaniment.

Perform a solo or soli during your *first* holiday concert!

You'll find at least one other harmonization part in this book.

Play duets with A and B parts.
Combine Melody , A , B , C and D parts in the full band.
Create ensembles with your friends in band and choir!

A BEST IN CLASS CHRISTMAS includes our lively new Christmas song, **Santa's Sleighride**, plus ten other holiday favorites.

Happy holidays and best wishes always,

Bruce Pearson

Chuck Elledge

Bruce Pearson

Chuck Elledge

ISBN 0-8497-8383-6

Jolly Old St. Nick

Traditional American carol

We Three Kings

John Henry Hopkins

We three kings of O - ri - ent are, Bear - ing gifts we tra - verse a - far. Field and foun - tain, moor and moun - tain fol - low - ing yon - der star. Oh, Star of won - der star of might, Star with roy - al beau - ty bright, West - ward lead - ing, still pro - ceed - ing, Guide us to the per - fect light.

Santa's Sleighride

Music by Chuck Elledge
Lyrics by Bruce Pearson

Up on the Housetop

Clement Clark Moore

O Tannenbaum
(O Christmas Tree)

Traditional German carol

O Tan-nen-baum, O Tan-nen-baum, How ev - er-green your bran - ches, O Tan - nen- baum, O Tan - nen- baum, How ev - er- green your bran - ches, Your need - les firm do ev - er shine, In win - ter, spring, and sum-mer- time, O Tan - nen- baum, O Tan - nen- baum, How ev - er- green your bran - ches. Such joy to all you now do bring, And ev' - ry-one will dance and sing, O Tan-nen-baum,O Tan-nen-baum,You are so ver - y pleas - ing.

Angels We Have Heard on High

W8CL

Deck the Halls

Traditional Welsh carol

Deck the halls with boughs of hol - ly,
Fa - la - la - la - la - la - la - la - la, 'Tis the sea - son to be jol - ly,
Fa - la - la - la - la - la - la - la - la. Don we now our gay ap - par - el,
Fa - la - la - la - la - la - la - la. Troll the an - cient Yule - tide car - ol,
Fa - la - la - la - la - la - la - la - la. Deck the halls with boughs of hol - ly,
Fa - la - la - la - la - la - la - la, Fa - la - la - la - la, Fa - la - la - la - la - la,
Fa - la - la - la - la - la - la - la - la.

W8CL

W8CL

O Come, All Ye Faithful

John Francis Wade

We Wish You a Merry Christmas

Traditional English carol

W8CL

W8CL

Whence Comes This Rush of Wings

Traditional French carol

W8CL

W8CL

Go Tell It on the Mountain

Black American Spiritual

W8CL

Performance Notes

Jolly Old St. Nick is an old American carol which describes a secret conversation with Santa just before Christmas. Lightly articulate quarter notes to bounce this happy tune. During second and third year band studies, you may wish to perform this piece in cut time.

The mixture of modes used by American composer John Henry Hopkins *(1820-1891)* gives **We Three Kings** a Medieval sound. Long half notes, shorter quarter notes and careful attention to the *crescendo* and *decrescendo* markings will enhance the performance of this arrangement.

Santa's Sleighride is a lively new carol which captures the anticipation of children on Christmas Eve. Creative use of several percussion instruments which imitate the sounds of toys simply add to the fun and excitement. Be sure to include singing on this original tune!

Clement Clark Moore's poem "A Visit from St. Nicholas" provides the text for the traditional American carol **Up on the Housetop**. Play half notes with full duration, and lightly tongue quarter and eighth notes with short, crisp articulations. During second and third year band studies, you may wish to perform this piece in cut time.

O Tannenbaum (O Christmas Tree) is one of the best loved carols in Germany. Its origin remains obscure, but sources indicate that the melody may date from the Middle Ages. This arrangement should be performed in a sensitive, gentle manner giving careful attention to the dynamics and phrase markings.

Angels We Have Heard on High dates from 18th century France. Traditionally, it is believed that the melody was first sung by shepherds watching over their fields on Christmas Eve. Be certain to perform the *Gloria in excelsis Deo* phrases in a smooth and lyrical manner.

The melody of **Deck the Halls** is an old Welsh tune. The words describe the custom of decorating banquet halls with holly, ivy and mistletoe during the winter Yule festival, commonly celebrated in the British Isles for centuries. Lightly articulate all tongued notes in this setting.

John Francis Wade *(1712-1786)* is credited with writing **O Come, All Ye Faithful**. The carol has also been labeled the "Portuguese Hymn" because the earliest known use of these words occurred in the chapel of London's Portuguese Embassy at the end of the 18th century. In this arrangement, sustain all half and quarter notes for full duration. Eighth notes should be played in a short, *staccato* manner.

We Wish You a Merry Christmas is a traditional English carol describing the custom of caroling and bringing good cheer throughout the holiday season. Performers should follow the dynamic and phrase markings very carefully in this lyrical setting.

The modal melody of **Whence Comes This Rush of Wings** is at least four hundred years old. The carol originated in southern France near the Spanish border. Performers should identify and bring out the theme and variations found in this arrangement.

Go Tell It on the Mountain is a lively and powerful Black American spiritual. The melody dates from the early 1800's. It is traditional to have a leader begin this piece with a group joining in on the refrain. Be certain to count and clap all rhythms in this piece. During second and third year band studies, you may wish to perform this selection in cut time.